The House Book

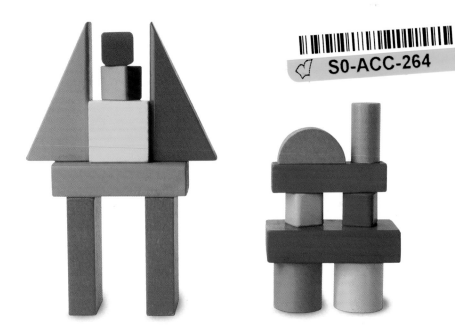

written by Shirley Frederick

Harcourt

Orlando   Boston   Dallas   Chicago   San Diego

www.harcourtschool.com

S0-ACC-264

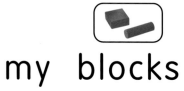

my blocks

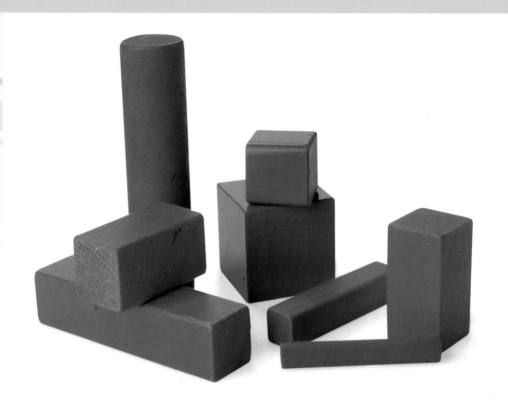

your blocks

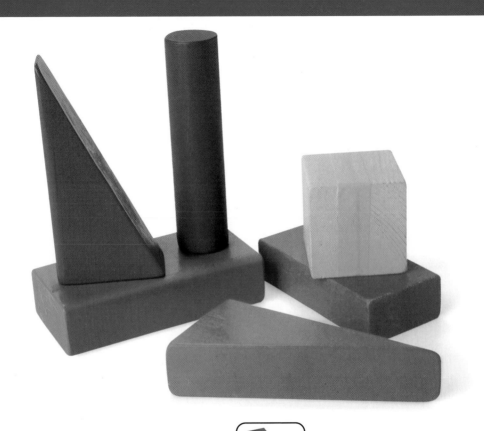

my blocks

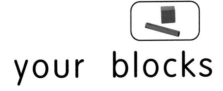

your blocks

 my blocks

your blocks

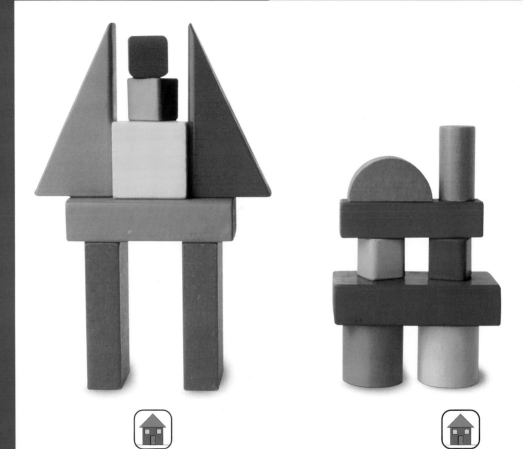

my house and your house